CW00392478

jazzy

piano ②

Brian Bonsor & Geoffry Russell-Smith

www.**universal**edition.com
vienna · london · new york

UE 19 363
ISMN 979-0-008-04527-1
UPC 8-03452-00951-1
ISBN 978-3-7024-1193-0

JAZZY SERIES

Young players of today are exposed to a variety of contemporary styles and this new series of jazzy and relaxing pieces for PIANO, FLUTE, CLARINET, SAXOPHONE, RECORDER and VIOLIN, attempts to provide players with experience of the syncopated patterns of Jazz, Rock and Pop music, whilst keeping within technical bounds which will have been achieved at various grades. Where appropriate, accompaniments have been kept deliberately simple to encourage other young players to act in this capacity.

Heutige junge Musiker sind einer Vielfalt zeitgenössischer Stile ausgesetzt. Diese neue Serie von jazzigen und entspannenden Stücken für KLAVIER, FLÖTE, KLARINETTE, SAXOPHON, BLOCKFLÖTE und VIOLINE, will versuchen, die Spieler mit der Praxis der synkopierten Muster in Jazz, Rock- und Popmusik vertraut zu machen, innerhalb der technischen Möglichkeiten, die schrittweise erreicht werden sollen.
Wo es zweckmäßig schien, wurden die Begleitstimmen absichtlich einfach gesetzt, um dadurch andere junge Musiker zum Mitspielen anzuregen.

JAZZY PIANO 2 *by* BRIAN BONSOR & GEOFFRY RUSSELL-SMITH

These pieces explore the enriched harmonies of the classical jazz era but with young hands in mind. A romantic rubato relaxed swing style suits most and, where applicable, the RH should sing over supporting chords.

JAZZY PIANO 2 *von* BRIAN BONSOR & GEOFFRY RUSSELL-SMITH

Diese Stücke erforschen die reiche harmonische Welt der klassischen Jazzära, sind jedoch vor allem für Spieler mit kleinen Händen gedacht. Sie sollten frei und locker-swingend gespielt werden. An geeigneten Stellen lasse man die rechte Hand über den tragenden Akkorden singen.

CONTENTS

JAZZY PIANO 2

WISTFUL PRELUDE

Relaxed unhurried phrases will enhance the romantic feel of this piece with the LH providing harmonic support for the melody.

Alle musikalischen Phrasen sollten locker und ruhig ausgespielt werden, um die romantische Note dieses Stücks voll zur Geltung zu bringen. Die Harmonien in der linken Hand bilden die Grundlage für die Melodie.

Andante rubato (♩ = c. 72)

GEOFFRY RUSSELL-SMITH

Universal Edition UE 19363

rall.   Tempo I

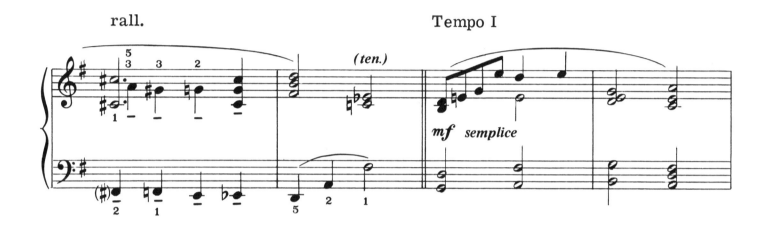

rit.

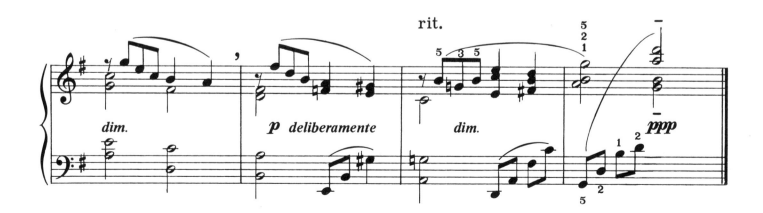

② GIRL ON A CAT-WALK

If smaller hands need to spread the LH tenth*, anticipate the beat with the lower note and make sure the upper note is on the beat itself.

Soll die Dezime in der linken Hand* von kleinen Händen gegriffen werden, so kann zur Erleichterung die untere Note vorgeschlagen werden. Die obere Note muß genau auf Schlag kommen.

Medium blues tempo (♩ = 84) (♪♪ = ♩♪ throughout)

GEOFFRY RUSSELL-SMITH

* spread if necessary

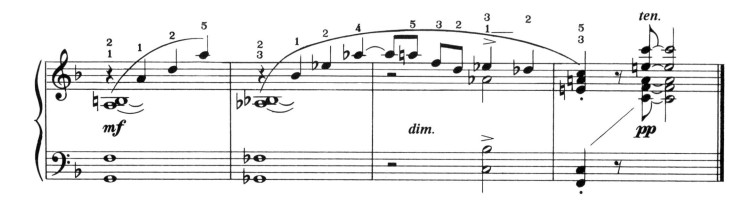

FEELIN' GOOD

♪♩ = ♩♪ throughout, but all quavers are to be played 'straight'. Use a light, crisp touch except in bars 17-25 which, for contrast, need a warmer, broader sound. Pedal only where indicated. Notes in brackets may be omitted.

♪♩ ist im ganzen Stück als ♩♪ auszuführen. Die Achtelnoten sind jedoch streng rhythmisch zu spielen. Der Anschlag sollte leicht und knapp sein, mit Ausnahme der Takte 17-25, die durch ihren wärmeren, breiteren Klang einen Kontrast zum Rest des Stückes bilden müssen. Pedal nur an den angegebenen Stellen verwenden. Noten in Klammern können weggelassen werden.

BRIAN BONSOR

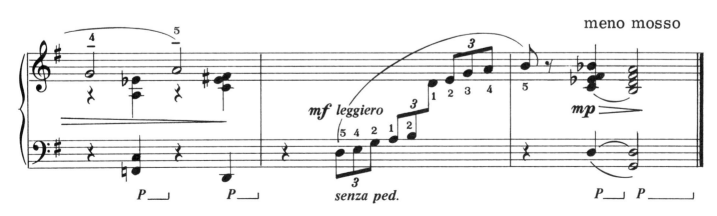

4

WILLIE WAGGLESTICK'S WALKABOUT

Some LH jazz patterns have been modified to suit small hands. The 3 against 2 passage (bars 22-24) can be worked out like this:

Einige Jazzfiguren in der linken Hand wurden abgeändert und auf die Bedürfnisse kleiner Hände zugeschnitten. Die Stelle von Takt 22-24, in der 3 gegen 2 zu spielen sind, kann folgendermaßen erarbeitet werden:

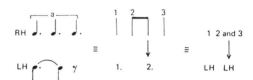

Notes in brackets may be omitted.   Noten in Klammern können weggelassen werden.

BRIAN BONSOR

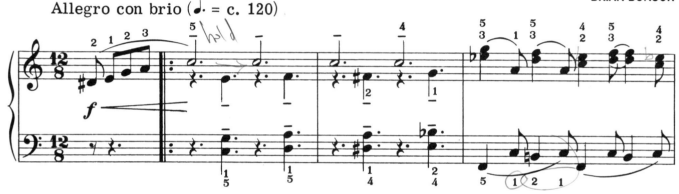

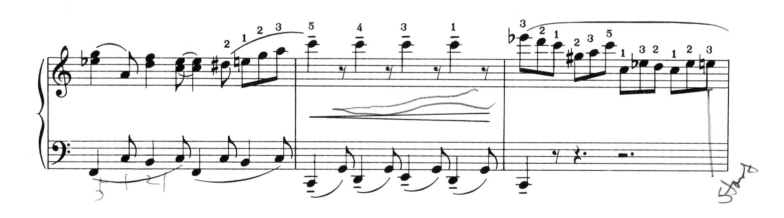

rit. e dim.

molto rit.

rit. e dim.   molto rit.

DREAMY

As in 'Feelin' Good', throughout this gently swinging piece but all pairs of quavers should be played equal. Let the right hand sing! Notes in brackets may be omitted.

Gleich wie in "Feeling' Good", ist auch in diesem sanft swingenden Stück immer als auszuführen. Die Achtelpaare dagegen sind streng im Rhythmus zu spielen. Die rechte Hand muß singen! Noten in Klammern können weggelassen werden.

BRIAN BONSOR